The Brothers Grimm

Retold by Jenny Dooley & Chris Bates

Stage 1   Pupil's Book

Express Publishing

Published by Express Publishing

Liberty House, Greenham Business Park, Newbury,
Berkshire RG19 6HW, United Kingdom
Tel.: (0044) 1635 817 363
Fax: (0044) 1635 817 463
email: inquiries@expresspublishing.co.uk
www.expresspublishing.co.uk

Colour Illustrations: Lucas

Music by Ted & Taz © Express Publishing, 2004

First published 2004
Published in this edition 2007
Tenth impression 2018

Made in EU

ISBN 978-1-84558-088-9

CONTENTS

snow

winter

Queen **King** **Princess**

garden

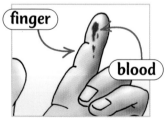

flower **bud**

pick

finger **blood**

4

It's winter and it's snowing, a long long time ago.
The Queen is in her garden, looking at the snow.
"I want to pick some flowers. Oh, look! A pretty bud!
Oh, no! My little finger! And look! A drop of blood!"

5

baby

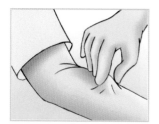

skin

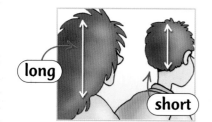

long short

hair

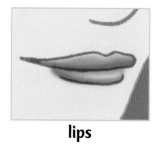

lips

pretty ugly

6

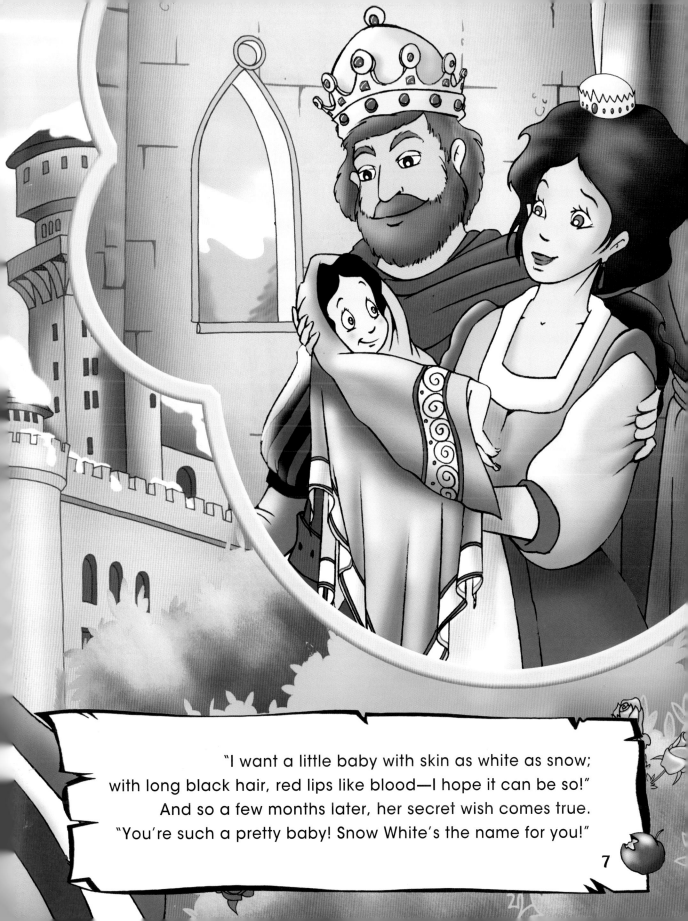

"I want a little baby with skin as white as snow;
with long black hair, red lips like blood—I hope it can be so!"
And so a few months later, her secret wish comes true.
"You're such a pretty baby! Snow White's the name for you!"

sick

die

cry

wife

husband

good

evil

But only two weeks after, the Queen gets sick and dies.
The King is very lonely and every day he cries.
"My baby needs a mother, so this is my new wife."
"She's beautiful, but evil ..." "... and has a secret life!"

9

magic

wall

mirror

talk

look into

hear

"She's got a magic mirror! She talks to it each day."

"She looks into the mirror and then I hear her say:"

"Mirror, mirror, on the wall, who's the prettiest one of all?"

"I cannot lie, so I must say you're the prettiest one today!"

happy

sad

For sixteen years she's happy—the mirror says the same.
But then one day the mirror gives her another name.
"Mirror, mirror, on the wall, who's the prettiest one of all?"
"I cannot lie, so I must say Snow White's the prettiest today!"

13

angry

call guard

forest take

bring

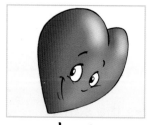

heart

14

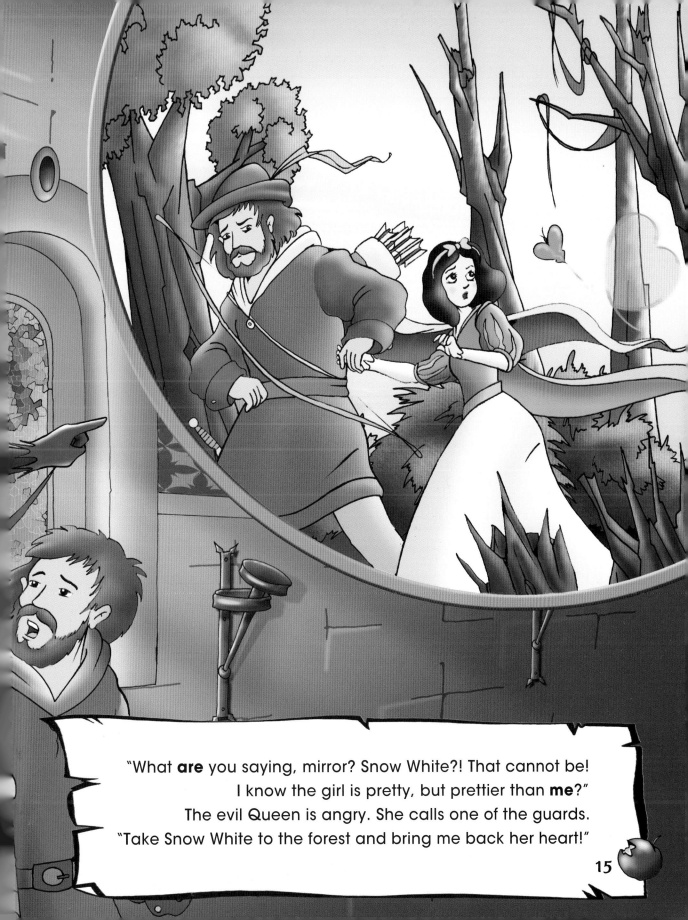

"What **are** you saying, mirror? Snow White?! That cannot be!
I know the girl is pretty, but prettier than **me**?"
The evil Queen is angry. She calls one of the guards.
"Take Snow White to the forest and bring me back her heart!"

15

The Evil Queen

Chorus: The Evil Queen!
             The Evil Queen!
             She is so bad!
             She is so mean!

Oh, poor Snow White!
Oh, poor Snow White!
Where can you run?
Where can you hide?

Repeat chorus

The guard is sad.
He wants to cry.
He doesn't want
Snow White to die!

Repeat chorus

16

arrow

kill

run

deer

put in

sack

 18

"Why have you got an arrow?" "The Queen wants you to die!"
"Oh please, sir, please don't kill me!" "My dear Princess, don't cry.
I know the Queen is evil, so run and don't come back!"
And so he takes a deer's heart and puts it in his sack.

smart / clever

give

cold

alone

find

20

The guard is very clever! His plan is very smart.
"I hope my Queen is happy." "Oh, yes! Give me the heart!"
But Snow White's in the forest. "I'm cold and all alone."
She walks and walks for hours and finds a little home.

The Home of the Seven Dwarfs

What a lovely little house!
And everything's so small!
Tiny chairs and tiny beds—
there's nothing big at all!

Chorus: The home of the seven dwarfs—
so small in every way!
The home of the seven dwarfs—
a lovely place to stay!

What a lovely little house!
But no one is inside!
The dwarfs work hard all day long
and come back home at night.

Repeat chorus

huge tiny

sleepy

rest

bed

sleep

24

"This house is very tiny and everything's so small!
But where is everybody? There's no one here at all!"
Snow White is very sleepy. She needs a little rest.
"I need a bed to sleep on. Ah yes! This is the best!"

dwarf

ribbon

dress

snowflake

The seven dwarfs come home now and then they find Snow White.
"This girl is very pretty!" "Why is she here tonight?"
"Oh, look at all her ribbons!" "And what a pretty dress!"
"Her skin is white like snowflakes!" "She must be a princess!"

wake up

welcome

kind

mean

 28

"I think she's waking up now." "You're welcome here, my dear!"
"Please tell us where you come from." "And tell us why you're here!"
"My father's wife is evil." "Who is she?" "She's the Queen!
And now she wants to kill me." "Oh, no! That's very mean!"

29

worry

hide

far away

stranger

"Don't worry! You can hide here. The Queen is far away!"
"Oh, thank you! I'm so happy! I don't know what to say!"
"But promise to be careful!" "And stay inside, my dear."
"Don't ever talk to strangers!" "Don't ever let them near!"

surprise

But then a few months later, the Queen gets a surprise.
"She's talking to the mirror." "It never tells her lies!"
"Mirror, mirror, on the wall, who's the prettiest one of all?"
"I cannot lie, so I must say Snow White's the prettiest today!"

33

dead

hill

face

paint

put on

rags

day

night

"But she is dead! That cannot be! She can't be prettier than me!"
"Over the hills and far away, she lives with seven dwarfs this day!"
The Queen is very angry. "Just wait and see, Snow White!"
She paints her face and puts on rags and walks into the night.

morning

door

knock

buy

rich

poor

tasty

She finds the house next morning. "Who's knocking on the door?"
"Please buy some of my apples. You see, I'm very poor!"
"I'm really very sorry. I can't open the door."
"But look at these nice apples! They're tasty! Are you sure?"

bite

fall down

poison

38

"All right then, let me try one." "Please take this red one here."
"You're right! It looks so tasty!" "Then take a bite, my dear!"
But when she bites the apple, she falls down on the floor.
"The apple's full of poison! Now Snow White's dead, I'm sure!"

fall in

river

The dwarfs are coming home now. They see the evil Queen.
"Is that the Queen I see there?" "She looks so very mean!"
"She's running to the forest!" "Come on, let's go there, too!"
"She's falling in the river!" "Now, that's the end of you!"

41

together

look

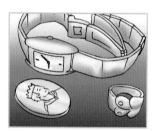

golden

42

They all go home together. "Snow White, we're home, my dear!"
"Where is our little Princess?" "Oh, no! Look over here!"
"Our Princess isn't sleeping!" "I think Snow White is dead!"
And then they make their Princess a pretty golden bed.

43

The Spell

Oh, dear Snow White,
you are not dead—
it's just an evil spell!
Your one true love
can wake you up
and then all will be well!

A handsome prince
is on his way—
he's on a big white horse.
His magic kiss
will wake you up
and break the spell, of course!

around

watch

minute

The seven dwarfs are sad now. They stand around the bed.
"She looks so very pretty." "I can't believe she's dead!"
They stay out in the forest and watch her day and night.
And every single minute, they cry for their Snow White.

47

ride

handsome ugly

strong

kiss

48

One day a prince comes riding. He's on a big white horse.
He's very tall and handsome, and strong, and kind, of course!
"It says here she's a princess ... but why is she like this?
She looks so very pretty!" He gives Snow White a kiss.

eyes

marry

50

"Look at that man! Who is he?" "He's kissing our Snow White!"
"But look! Her eyes are open!" "I think that she's all right!"
"Who are you?" "I'm Prince Henry." "What are you doing here?"
"Snow White, I think I love you. Please marry me, my dear!"

go away

celebrate

"I'll marry you, Prince Henry!" "Snow White, don't go away!"
"But you can all come with us!" "Let's celebrate! Hurray!"
Snow White goes with Prince Henry and takes her seven friends.
Now everybody's happy and so, this is the END!

Never Talk to Strangers!

Never talk to strangers,
no matter what you do!
They're not your friends!
You don't know them!
They can be mean to you!

Don't take things from strangers!
No apples, cakes or sweets!
You must say "No"
and walk away!
You don't need any treats!

Never go with strangers!
You must say "No, no, no"!
They may look nice,
they may look kind—
don't go with them! Don't go!

ACTIVITIES

Activities for pages 4 – 11

A Look at the pictures and match them with the words.

mirror

finger

bud

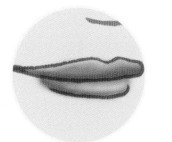

skin

lips

winter

B Can you find these words in the puzzle?

~~garden~~   magic

queen   baby

evil   blood

die   hair

hear   talk

snow   wife

O	G	P	W	I	F	E	Z	J	H	C
M	A	G	I	C	I	Q	U	E	E	N
L	R	S	K	T	V	K	T	S	A	A
B	D	Z	B	A	B	Y	H	N	R	J
X	E	V	I	L	O	B	L	O	O	D
X	N	R	F	K	Q	C	U	W	X	I
A	P	V	Y	H	A	I	R	O	D	E

C Look at the pictures and fill in the missing letters to complete the words.

0   f_l_ower

1   pr__ncess

2   wal__

3   k__ng

4   hus__and

5   gar__en

D Look at the pictures and (circle) the correct word.

0
(**a**) happy
b ugly

1
a sick
b cold

2
a sad
b alone

3
a pretty
b angry

4
a short
b alone

5
a cold
b clever

E Look at the pictures and letters and write the words.

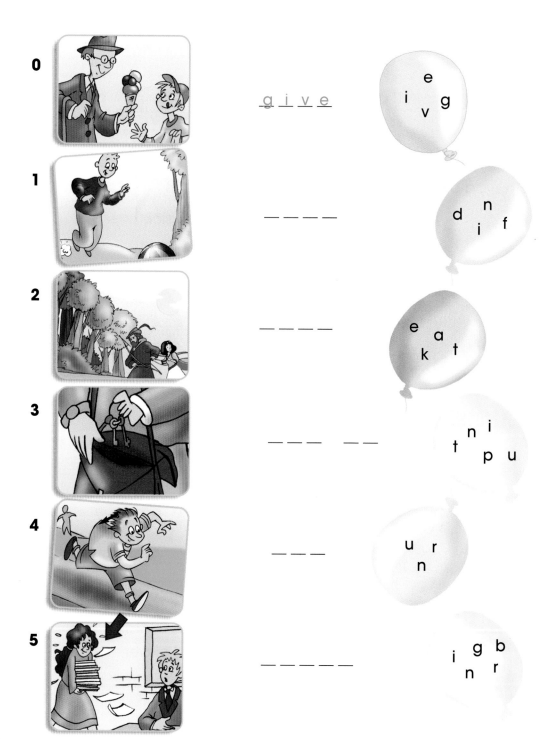

0 g i v e

1 _ _ _ _

2 _ _ _ _

3 _ _ _   _ _

4 _ _ _

5 _ _ _ _ _

58

F **Look and read. Write** yes **or** no**.**

0 The ribbon is yellow.   ...no...

1 This is a blue dress.   ....

2 This man is sleepy.   ....

3 This mouse is huge.   ....

4 The boat is very far away.   ....

5 The boy is very mean.   ....

G **Look at the pictures. Then write the words to complete the sentences.**

0 She is  ....resting........ in the armchair.

1 He is  .... on the bed.

2 He is  ....

3 He is  .... from his friends.

4 She is  .... about the cat.

5 She is  .... a guard.

60

H Listen. Then, look at the picture and the letters and write the words.

0 The Evil Queen is wearing ....rags.......... .

1 The .... are not with Snow White.

2 The Evil Queen wants Snow White to
   .... the apples.

3 The apple looks so .... !

4 Snow White isn't opening the ....

s r g a
w r a f s d

u b y
y s a t t
o r o d

I Circle the words.

surprisehillfacepoisondayfloor

Activities for pages 40 – 49

J Look and copy.

She is looking at the kite.   He is painting his face.

He is putting on his hat.   He is knocking on the door.

He is falling in the river.   It is dying.

0

He is falling
in the river.

1

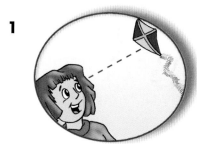

....
....

2

....
....

3

....
....

4

....
....

5

....
....

K **a) Read this first:**

Yes, they are.
No, they aren't.

Yes, he is.
No, he isn't.

Yes, she is.
No, she isn't.

b) Look and read. Then, write the answers.

0 Snow White is talking to the Dwarfs. ....No, she isn't.......

1 The dwarfs are around Snow White. ....

2 The Prince is handsome and strong. ....

3 The dwarfs are sitting together. ....

4 Snow White is sitting on a golden bed. ....

5 The Prince is on a big black horse. ....

6 Snow White is sad. ....

Activities for the whole story

L Look at the pictures and fill in the puzzle.

The secret words are: _ _ _ _ _ _   _ _ _ _ _ _

M **Who says what? Listen and write.**

Evil Queen

King

Prince

Good Queen

Snow White

Mirror

Dwarfs

0 "I want a little baby
with skin as white as snow."   Good Queen

1 "You're such a pretty baby!
Snow White's the name for you!"   ....

2 "... you're the prettiest one today!"   ....

3 "I'm really very sorry; I can't open the door." ....

4 "The apple's full of poison!
Now Snow White's dead, I'm sure!"   ....

5 "She looks so very pretty."
"I can't believe she's dead!"   ....

6 "Snow White, I think I love you."   ....

65

N **Write the words and match them to make rhyming pairs.**

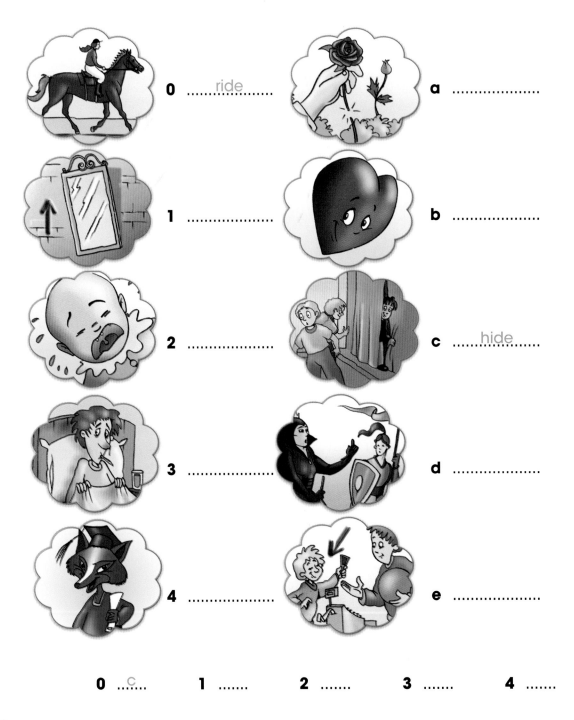

0 ....ride..........   a ....

1 ....   b ....

2 ....   c ....hide.......

3 ....   d ....

4 ....   e ....

0 ...c....   1 ......   2 ......   3 ......   4 ......

O **Match the pictures to their opposites.**

0 ...c... **1** .... **2** .... **3** .... **4** .... **5** ....

67

P **Look and write. Then, tick (✔) the odd-one-out and say.**

........marry........ ....eyes........ ....celebrate........

Q **Look at the pictures and read the sentences. Put a tick (✓) or cross (✗).**

0 This is a guard.

3 This is a baby.

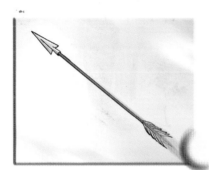

1 This is a bed.

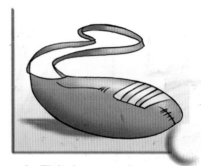

4 This is a sack.

2 This is a deer.

5 This is a horse.

R Read the number key and colour the picture.

1	light blue	**7**	brown
2	blue	**8**	light brown
3	yellow	**9**	light green
4	orange	**10**	dark green
5	red	**11**	black
6	light orange	**12**	pink

70

▶ Now, let's act it out!

Actors:
King
Good Queen
Evil Queen
Snow White
Prince
7 dwarfs
Servant 1
Servant 2
Guard
Magic Mirror

Narrator(s): One, or as many pupils as necessary, dressed as princes/princesses.

Scene 1
(At the palace)

Narrator: It's winter and it's snowing,
a long long time ago.
The Queen is in her garden,
looking at the snow.

Good Queen: I want to pick some flowers.
Oh, look! A pretty bud!
Oh, no! My little finger!
And look! A drop of blood!

I want a little baby
with skin as white as snow;
with long black hair,
red lips like blood—
I hope it can be so!

Narrator: And so a few months later,
her secret wish comes true.

King:	You're such a pretty baby! Snow White's the name for you!
Narrator:	But only two weeks after, the Queen gets sick and dies. The King is very lonely and every day he cries.
King:	My baby needs a mother, so this is my new wife.
Servant 1:	She's beautiful, but evil …
Servant 2:	… and has a secret life!
Servant 1:	She's got a magic mirror! She talks to it each day.
Servant 2:	She looks into the mirror and then I hear her say:
Evil Queen:	Mirror, mirror, on the wall, who's the prettiest one of all?
Mirror:	I cannot lie, so I must say you're the prettiest one today!
Narrator:	For sixteen years she's happy— the mirror says the same. But then one day the mirror gives her another name.
Evil Queen:	Mirror, mirror, on the wall, who's the prettiest one of all?

| **Mirror:** | I cannot lie, so I must say |
| | Snow White's the prettiest today! |

Evil Queen:	What **are** you saying, mirror?
	Snow White?! That cannot be!
	I know the girl is pretty,
	but prettier than **me**?

| **Narrator:** | The evil Queen is angry. |
| | She calls one of the guards. |

| **Evil Queen:** | Take Snow White to the forest |
| | and bring me back her heart! |

Song: The Evil Queen

Chorus:	The Evil Queen!
	The Evil Queen!
	She is so bad!
	She is so mean!

Oh, poor Snow White!
Oh, poor Snow White!
Where can you run?
Where can you hide?

Repeat chorus

The guard is sad.
He wants to cry.
He doesn't want
Snow White to die!

Repeat chorus

Scene 2
(At the forest)

Snow White:	Why have you got an arrow?
Guard:	The Queen wants you to die!
Snow White:	Oh please, sir, please don't kill me!
Guard:	My dear Princess, don't cry. I know the Queen is evil, so run and don't come back!
Narrator:	And so he takes a deer's heart and puts it in his sack. The guard is very clever! His plan is very smart.
Guard:	I hope my Queen is happy.
Evil Queen:	Oh, yes! Give me the heart!
Narrator:	But Snow White's in the forest.
Snow White:	I'm cold and all alone.
Narrator:	She walks and walks for hours and finds a little home.

Song: The Home of the Seven Dwarfs

What a lovely little house!
And everything's so small!
Tiny chairs and tiny beds–
there's nothing big at all!

Chorus: The home of the seven dwarfs—
so small in every way!
The home of the seven dwarfs—
a lovely place to stay!

What a lovely little house!
But no one is inside!
The dwarfs work hard all day long
and come back home at night.

Repeat chorus

Scene 3
(At the dwarfs' house)

Snow White: This house is very tiny
and everything's so small!
But where is everybody?
There's no one here at all!

Narrator: Snow White is very sleepy.
She needs a little rest.

Snow White: I need a bed to sleep on.
Ah yes! This is the best!

Narrator: The seven dwarfs come home now
and then they find Snow White.

Dwarf 1: This girl is very pretty!

Dwarf 2: Why is she here tonight?

Dwarf 3: Oh, look at all her ribbons!

Dwarf 4: And what a pretty dress!

Dwarf 5: Her skin is white like snowflakes!

Dwarf 6: She must be a princess!

Dwarf 7: I think she's waking up now.

Dwarf 1: You're welcome here, my dear!

Dwarf 2:	Please tell us where you come from.
Dwarf 3:	And tell us why you're here!
Snow White:	My father's wife is evil.
All Dwarfs:	Who is she?
Snow White:	She's the Queen! And now she wants to kill me.
All Dwarfs:	Oh, no! That's very mean!
Dwarf 4:	Don't worry! You can hide here. The Queen is far away!
Snow White:	Oh, thank you! I'm so happy! I don't know what to say!
Dwarf 5:	But promise to be careful!
Dwarf 6:	And stay inside, my dear.
Dwarf 7:	Don't ever talk to strangers!
Dwarf 1:	Don't ever let them near!
Narrator:	But then a few months later, the Queen gets a surprise.
Servant 1:	She's talking to the mirror.
Servant 2:	It never tells her lies!

Evil Queen: Mirror, mirror, on the wall,
who's the prettiest one of all?

Mirror: I cannot lie, so I must say
Snow White's the prettiest today!

Evil Queen: But she is dead! That cannot be!
She can't be prettier than me!

Mirror: Over the hills and far away,
she lives with seven dwarfs this day!

Narrator: The Queen is very angry.

Evil Queen: Just wait and see, Snow White!

Narrator: She paints her face
and puts on rags
and walks into the night.

She finds the house next morning.

Snow White: Who's knocking on the door?

Evil Queen: Please buy some of my apples.
You see, I'm very poor!

Snow White: I'm really very sorry.
I can't open the door.

Evil Queen: But look at these nice apples!
They're tasty! Are you sure?

Snow White: All right then, let me try one.

Evil Queen: Please take this red one here.

Snow White: You're right! It looks so tasty!

Evil Queen: Then take a bite, my dear!

Narrator: But when she bites the apple, she falls down on the floor.

Evil Queen: The apple's full of poison! Now Snow White's dead, I'm sure!

Narrator: The dwarfs are coming home now. They see the evil Queen.

Dwarf 2: Is that the Queen I see there?

Dwarf 3: She looks so very mean!

Dwarf 4: She's running to the forest!

Dwarf 5: Come on, let's go there, too!

Dwarf 6: She's falling in the river!

Dwarf 7: Now, that's the end of you!

Narrator: They all go home together.

Dwarf 1: Snow White, we're home, my dear!

Dwarf 2:   Where is our little Princess?

Dwarf 3:   Oh, no! Look over here!

Dwarf 4:   Our Princess isn't sleeping!

Dwarf 5:   I think Snow White is dead!

Narrator: And then they make their Princess
a pretty golden bed.

Song: The Spell

Oh, dear Snow White,
you are not dead—
it's just an evil spell!
Your one true love
can wake you up
and then all will be well!

A handsome prince
is on his way—
he's on a big white horse.
His magic kiss
will wake you up
and break the spell, of course!

Scene 4
(In the forest)

Narrator:	The seven dwarfs are sad now. They stand around the bed.
Dwarf 6:	She looks so very pretty.
Dwarf 7:	I can't believe she's dead!
Narrator:	They stay out in the forest and watch her day and night. And every single minute, they cry for their Snow White. One day a prince comes riding. He's on a big white horse. He's very tall and handsome, and strong, and kind, of course!
Prince:	It says here she's a princess … but why is she like this? She looks so very pretty!
Narrator:	He gives Snow White a kiss.
Dwarf 1:	Look at that man! Who is he?
Dwarf 2:	He's kissing our Snow White!
Dwarf 3:	But look! Her eyes are open!
Dwarf 4:	I think that she's all right!

Snow White:	Who are you?
Prince:	I'm Prince Henry.
Snow White:	What are you doing here?
Prince:	Snow White, I think I love you. Please marry me, my dear!
Snow White:	I'll marry you, Prince Henry!
All Dwarfs:	Snow White, don't go away!
Prince:	But you can all come with us!
All Dwarfs:	Let's celebrate! Hurray!
Narrator:	Snow White goes with Prince Henry and takes her seven friends. Now everybody's happy and so, this is the END!

Song: Never Talk to Strangers!

Never talk to strangers,
no matter what you do!
They're not your friends!
You don't know them!
They can be mean to you!

Don't take things from strangers!
No apples, cakes or sweets!
You must say "No"
and walk away!
You don't need any treats!

Never go with strangers!
You must say "No, no, no"!
They may look nice,
they may look kind—
don't go with them! Don't go!

◗ Props

Props	SCENE 1	SCENE 2	SCENE 3	SCENE 4
rose bud	✓			
baby	✓			
bow and arrow		✓		
sack		✓		
basket of apples			✓	

Word List

The words in colour are presented in the picture dictionary of the main story.

a few months later	blood	door
a long time ago	bring	dress
after	bud	drop
all right	but	dwarf
alone	buy	each
angry	call	end
another	can	ever
apple	celebrate	every day
around	clever	every single minute
arrow	cold	everybody
at all	come back	everything
baby	come from	evil
back	come true	eyes
be careful	cry	face
beautiful	day	fall down
bed	dead	fall in
believe	dear	far away
big	deer	father
bite	die	find
black	do	finger

floor	home	live
flower	hope	lonely
forest	horse	long
friend	hour	look
full of	house	look at
garden	huge	look into
get	hurray!	love
girl	husband	magic
give	I'm sorry	make
go	inside	man
go away	just	marry
golden	kill	mean
good (better – the best)	kind	minute
guard	King	mirror
hair	kiss	morning
handsome	knock	mother
happy	know	must
have/has got	let	name
hear	let's	near
heart	lie	need
here	like	new
hide	lips	next
hill	little	nice

night	red	snowflake
no one	rest	so
now	ribbon	some
of course	rich	stand
one day	ride	stay
only	river	stranger
open	run	strong
out	sack	such
over	sad	sure
over here	say	surprise
paint	secret	take
pick	see	talk
plan	seven	tall
please	short	tasty
poison	sick	tell
poor	sir	thank you
pretty (prettier – the prettiest)	sixteen	That cannot be!
Princess	skin	the prettiest one
promise	sleep	the same
put in	sleepy	then
put on	small	there
Queen	smart	think
rags	snow	tiny

today	walk	white
together	wall	wife
tonight	want	winter
try	watch	wish
ugly	week	worry
wait	welcome	year
wake up	where	you're right